The Dolphins Swim Free

The story of the Atlantis dolphins

Marianne Rogers
Illustrated by Martin Thompson
Scientific adviser Dr Nick Gales

Kangaroo Press

Contents

Photographs courtesy of Nick Gales and Kelly Waples.

© Marianne Rogers and Martin Thompson 1994

First published in 1994 by Kangaroo Press Pty Ltd
3 Whitehall Road Kenthurst NSW 2156 Australia
P.O. Box 6125 Dural Delivery Centre NSW 2158
Typeset by G.T. Setters Pty Limited
Printed in China through Colorcraft Ltd

ISBN 0 86417 573 6

One in the Net

1

Between February and August of 1981 a group of
dolphins was caught off the coast of Western Australia.
These dolphins were of the species *Tursiops truncatus*,
which are generally known as Indian Ocean bottlenose
dolphins. They were destined for the Atlantis Marine
Park at Two Rocks, which is about sixty kilometres
north of Perth. Here, it was hoped, they would provide
a great tourist attraction.

It took over six months to catch all the dolphins.
They had to be treated gently and selected carefully to
make sure they were young enough to adapt to
captivity and each other, yet old enough to be
independent of maternal care. Three males, Rajah,
Nero and Frodo, and four females, Rani, Mila, Lulu
and Karleen, formed the original Atlantis family. From
their size it was estimated that they were between
three- and six-years-old. The exact age of the dolphins
of the Atlantis group did not need to be known for
their welfare.

The only way to accurately assess the age of dolphins
is to examine their teeth. A section through the tooth
of a dolphin will show layers laid down in the seasons,
much like the rings of wood in a tree. Measurements
taken from dolphins which died in captivity have
shown that the number of layers in a tooth corresponds
to the age of the dolphin. From measurements of dead
dolphins trapped in shark nets off the Natal coast of
South Africa, we know size will give a fairly good
estimate of age.

It has been found that larger individuals of the

Dolphins look friendly because the shape of their mouth cannot be altered like ours but instead is bent into what looks like a permanent grin.

species live in colder waters and smaller specimens in warmer waters. North Atlantic Ocean dolphins have broad faces. The famous Monkey Mia dolphins of north Western Australia are smaller animals. Despite these differences all these dolphins belong to the same species.

The Atlantis dolphins were caught by means of a special net called a break-away hoop net. A net attached to a hoop by means of a thin thread was dropped over the front of the dolphin while it was bow riding at the front of the boat. The hoop would break away from the net, which would then tighten slightly at the front so as to remain on the dolphin when it swam away. A line, about one hundred metres long and attached to the net, was played out from the boat. After a few minutes the dolphin recovered from the shock of the hoop passing over it and the net being on it.

Divers then entered the water and gently monitored the heart rate and breathing of each animal. Only one animal of the eight caught in this way showed signs of unusual distress—it held its breath. Normally, while stressed by being caught, a dolphin breathes every fifteen to thirty seconds. This one did not take a breath for sixty seconds. The net was removed immediately and the dolphin recovered and swam off quickly, having resumed normal breathing.

The seven other dolphins were taken into captivity. The divers swam each dolphin into a special sling and lifted it gently onto the boat to take it back to the pool at Atlantis. Throughout the capture and after it, Nick Gales, a veterinarian and marine biologist, has monitored the health and well-being of the dolphins.

Dolphins love to bow ride in the wave which forms at the front of a boat as it speeds through the water.

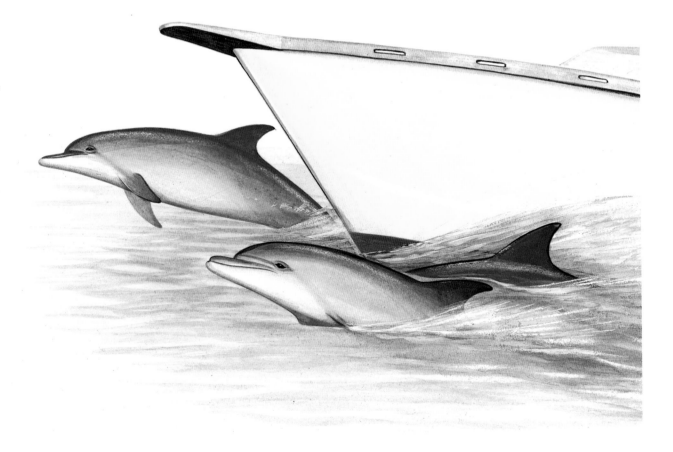

All of the dolphins were given names so they could be easily identified. Karleen, the first dolphin caught, was named after the boat which had been used for the capture. She was put in the pool at Atlantis with a turtle and given lots of attention by the trainers. Frodo was caught four days later, and they reacted positively together.

The two dolphins were happy to swim alongside each other. They synchronised their coming up to breathe and diving back down. This is a sign that dolphins are content with each other's company. A negative reaction is very obvious, as they will chase each other and often make a harsh sound. Each subsequent dolphin settled in more quickly and the group formed a harmonious unit.

Each of the dolphins had distinctive physical characteristics. Lulu was much lighter and Mila much darker than the other five. Lulu had a long rostrum (mouth area) and Karleen's rostrum was slightly

Anatomy of the dolphin.

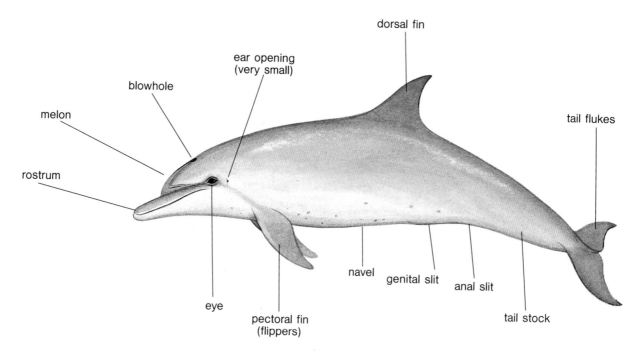

twisted. Rajah was a rotund fellow with a fat neck and a double chin. Both he and Rani had short rostrums and steep sloping melons, or foreheads. Frodo had a black beauty spot about three millimetres across on his left cheek and Nero had a little lump of flesh on his rostrum which looked like a limpet. This was the result of an old injury which had healed imperfectly. Dolphins touch objects, such as rocks, in their surroundings with their chins. Because of this many have chins which look a little battered, with scars and scrapes all over them.

The seven dolphins were allowed to swim around the pool. They were fed four times a day with specially chosen thawed frozen fish which were free of parasites. (Ten days at −30°C kills the parasite eggs.) The fish were snap frozen and had to be of good quality. The dolphins were dewormed and their health was carefully checked out. The trainers set about familiarising the dolphins with their presence.

Nick Gales' son Jeremy being introduced to Rajah.

2 *Getting Familiar*

In the first six months after the dolphins were captured they slowly settled in. They were thrown dead fish and they gradually discovered that the handlers would not harm them in any way. The dolphins became more confident and came closer and closer to the trainers for their fish until they were brave enough to take fish from the trainers' hands.

The sound of a whistle was introduced as a bridging signal. The whistle indicated when a dolphin had done what the handler wanted and could expect a fish as a reward. The whistle was blown before a dolphin was given a fish so it would associate the two events in that order. This would be valuable later on in the training

Kate, one of the trainers at Atlantis, training Mila. Note the whistle and the bucket of fish.

when it would be impossible to give a fish at the instant the dolphin performed the required behaviour. (We do a similar thing by saying 'good boy' to a dog when it is too far away to get a pat.) When a dolphin would not perform a trick which it had already learnt, the whistle would not be blown and a fish would not

One of the tricks that the dolphins used to perform regularly was the tail walk.

be given at that moment. No matter how the dolphins behaved, they would always receive their daily ration of fish by the end of the day. In other words, training was by positive reinforcement only.

As training went on the dolphins did not receive a fish every time they performed a feat. The frequency of rewards was reduced. They knew they would get some fish throughout the performance, but not after every feat.

Techniques for training were carefully selected and tried. Senior trainers would show new trainers the ropes. Many of them were outstanding trainers. Some of them would build up a terrific rapport with certain dolphins in their free time. It was important that the dolphins would be prepared to work with different people so staff changes and shifts would not affect the performances.

The first thing the dolphins were taught was to come and touch their trainer's hand. As a dolphin came closer to the outstretched palm of the trainer, the whistle was blown and the dolphin was given a fish

Kate with Rani and Frodo doing a slide out. Rani has her fluke held high.

from the trainer's other hand. The dolphin slowly came closer and closer to the hand until it could touch it. The whistle was blown immediately and the dolphin was given a fish. After a short while the dolphin would arrive very enthusiastically to touch an outstretched palm, knowing that this would bring approval. As trust grew the dolphins could be stroked on their sides or patted gently.

The handlers knew they must not touch the dolphins near their blowholes as this is an extremely sensitive area. Dolphins are wary as if they realise the vulnerability of their blowhole. Blindfolded dolphins can feel if their blowholes are clear of the water and if it is safe for them to breathe.

A long stick with a disk at the end was introduced as a target for teaching more advanced behaviour patterns. Initially it was used in the same way that the hand had been and the dolphin was rewarded for coming to the target. Because the target was on a stick, it could be moved. To teach the dolphins to jump out of the water, the target was slowly raised higher and higher. The dolphin was rewarded for jumping higher and higher to reach it. Finally the dolphin could jump up so high that its body would be completely out of the water, with a clearance of anything up to four and a half metres.

The same kind of target was used to teach the dolphins to leap out of the water and do a forward somersault. First the target was held up for the dolphin. When the dolphin was jumping out of the water, the target was moved slightly forward. The dolphin would move slightly forward to try and reach it. Each time it jumped up and moved further forward, the dolphin was rewarded. By a slow process, taking many steps, the dolphin would eventually leap out of

Another trainer, Ross, on Nero. This trick, known as a rocket ride, showed the incredible strength of the dolphins.

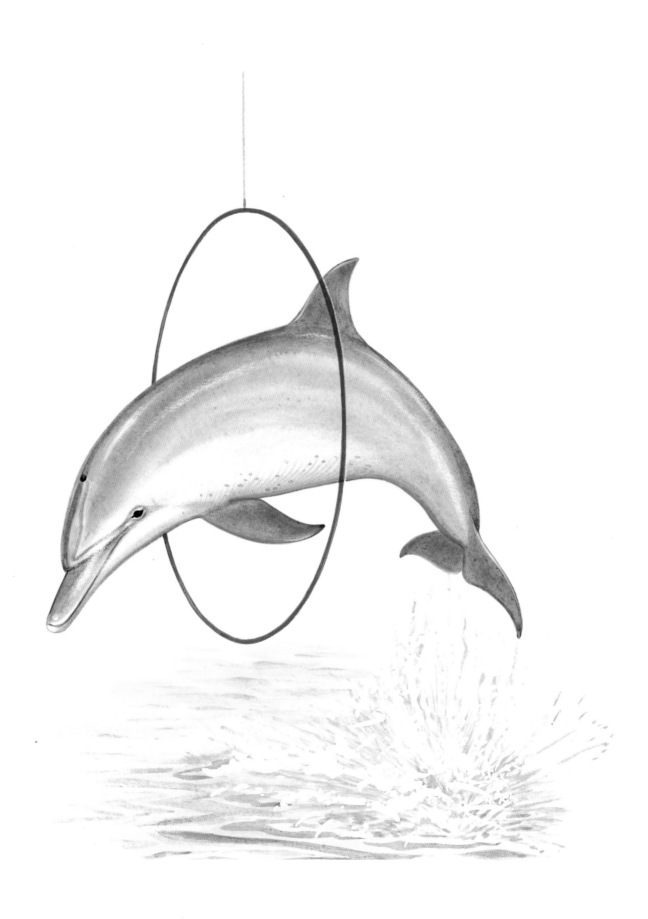

Nero (front) and Lulu do a bow at Atlantis Marine Park.

the water and do a complete forward somersault. Once the dolphin understood what was required, the target became unnecessary.

The dolphins were soon trained to perform many intricate actions for the public. They were conditioned to show many types of natural behaviour when commanded by their human trainers. Dolphins are very willing to please and by the reward training method they can be taught some very elaborate behaviour patterns (or tricks).

A dolphin leaping out from the water
to touch the ball suspended high above
the pool.

On Stage

3

Atlantis Marine Park opened to the public on 26 December 1981. In the first year over half a million people watched the dolphins give their show.

The dolphins performed two shows a day for the public but were actually worked four times each day. They were given a training session before and after public opening hours as it was not possible to train them to do new tricks during the shows.

The weather did not affect the pattern of shows or training. Shows were conducted even when there were only a few people watching. Occasionally, on special days like public holidays, there were three shows a day.

Every dolphin was worked in every show and the different characters of each dolphin soon became obvious: Karleen had a knack of wetting anyone with a camera; Rajah was ever so good at retrieving small objects but then he would hold them just out of range of the handler; and Frodo loved to open his mouth and have water dribbled into it.

Frodo was also very even-tempered, and if ever the audience was to interact with a dolphin, Frodo was chosen. Despite the popular belief that dolphins have a special regard for humans, they do not have inexhaustible patience and may well be annoyed by human activities. They are capable of giving a person a bite or a knock with their fluke. The latter is so strong that it is usually referred to as a 'kick', because it feels like a hard kick from a human.

Sometimes the dolphins would get bored or fed-up while trying to learn a new behaviour. The trainers would often give them a short break or reward them by allowing them to do a trick they particularly liked. This is known as *random interrupted reinforcement*. Karleen was always delighted when she was allowed to swim off and leap up to touch the ball that hung seven metres above the pool.

The dolphins appeared to have a sense of humour and often seemed to enjoy performing the tricks they had been taught. When there was a large vocal crowd voicing their appreciation, all the dolphins would put in an extra special effort.

They all had to be kept equally busy or they would get jealous of whoever was getting the attention. If one dolphin was being ignored for bad behaviour during a show, it would interfere with the others. For this reason, all the dolphins were given time out (or ignored) together. Normally five minutes of being ignored made all the dolphins happy to do what they were asked. The dolphins were not rewarded with fish

Kate feeding all the dolphins in the pool at Atlantis. Much of the animal husbandry was conducted underwater.

if they did not respond but, as explained before, they never went without their daily ration of fish.

All the dolphins were fed pretty much to appetite. This worked out to roughly five per cent of their body weight daily. Each dolphin had its own bucket into which its fish were carefully weighed out. A careful watch was kept on how much fish each dolphin ate and its weight and health were assessed every month. This was because a lack of appetite is generally the first sign of any illness or problem.

The regular weighing and measuring of the dolphins continued and it was noticed that Rani was putting on weight even though she was being fed her normal fish ration. It was decided to do an ultrasound on her to see if she was pregnant. The handler had Rani lie on her back for a few moments. The ultrasound showed what was thought to be a baby dolphin. Then all the other females were examined and they too seemed to

Kate and Ross steady Rani for an ultrasound examination while the other dolphins watch proceedings.

have something showing up on the machine. The ultrasound experts were called in as it appeared likely there might be a mistake—maybe they were looking at an organ present in all dolphins. No! No mistake—all four female dolphins were indeed pregnant!

A feeling of excitement rose as the days went by. The shows were stopped as the females needed the big show pool. The males were put into a smaller pool in case they interfered with the females or the soon-to-be-born baby dolphins. The males put on a modified show for the visiting public. Visitors could also view the pregnant females and were given an educational talk on dolphins. After the births visitors to the marine park would also be able to view the young dolphins, or calves.

The pregnant females were weighed and the foetal calves measured by ultrasound until between one and three months before birth. As soon as the females did not want to roll onto their backs for the ultrasound, they were no longer required to. At the end of the pregnancy term, which lasts about a year, the mothers were about forty per cent heavier than they had been before the start of their pregnancies.

In November 1988 Lulu was the first to give birth. Unfortunately her calf was stillborn. The autopsy carried out at Murdoch University showed that the calf was premature. The staff at Atlantis were now very worried about the calves to come. In January 1989 Rani gave birth to Echo; in March Mila gave birth to Nakita; and in April Karleen gave birth to Kia. All three calves were females.

The three calves were very playful and settled into the group very well. Their mothers all had voracious appetites as they produced the very rich milk for their calves. Dolphin milk is very high in fat and baby

Dolphin calves are generally born tail first. As they emerge they look rather strange, with creases in their skin. The fluke, or large tail fin, is often bent. Within a few hours it straightens out and the calves look like perfect miniature dolphins.

dolphins grow very rapidly. While the mothers were feeding their young the amount of fish that they ate increased to about eight per cent of their body weight per day.

Lulu seemed very interested in the three new calves after they were born. Everyone thought: 'Great! This is the "aunt" relationship we have all heard about in dolphins.' A female dolphin will often hang around another pregnant female to help at the time of birth and offers increased protection to mother and calf after the birth. Unfortunately Lulu was trying to push between Echo and her mother Rani. Perhaps she was jealous of another mother having a calf. By her actions she was effectively stopping Echo from feeding. Lulu was separated from the females and their calves to allow normal feeding to occur.

The young dolphins were all different: Nakita had a scar next to her blowhole and Echo had a mark next to her eye. Each of the mothers had different responses to their babies. Mila was always very much more protective of her calf than the other mothers. She would nudge Nakita back into line if she ever ventured too far away. Even when Nakita had grown quite large the handlers made sure they knew where Mila was before they approached Nakita. They were likely to receive a good 'kick' from Mila if they did not take care.

The three calves grew quickly. They were soon learning new behaviours and performing with the other dolphins. Being youngsters they were extra playful and exuberant and the audience was enthralled.

That the dolphins enjoyed their tricks was made obvious by the dolphin calves playing together using the tricks which they had been taught. One trick they really liked was to swim around the pool at a high

Rani with her baby Echo.

speed, leap out onto a special platform, spin around and plop back into the water. Unfortunately the calves playing the game did not always use the special platform near their pool. Instead they would leap out onto the concrete rim of the pool and spin around there.

One night the night watchman was alerted by the high pitched distress calls of a dolphin. He rushed to the pool and found Kia dangling just above the ground, unable to pull herself back into the pool. The watchman pushed her back into the pool and telephoned Nick. It was one o'clock in the morning and a fairly sleepy Nick asked if the dolphin was

A very young dolphin swimming with two adults.

swimming around normally. On hearing that she was, he decided to wait until morning before examining her. She seemed unhurt by her experience. In case a similar experience did not have such a fortunate ending, a small stainless steel fence was constructed around the rim of the pool.

Too Good to Last 4

The standards under which marine mammals were kept in captivity in Australia were rather poor in years gone by. Originally, in 1981, the US Marine Mammal Standard was applied in Australia. This stated that each dolphin required 22 cubic metres of water. These standards were updated in 1989 by CALM, the governmental authority in Western Australia for Conservation and Land Management. The new standards required 200 cubic metres of water per dolphin. This brought Western Australia into line with the latest data available from Europe.

The extra dolphin calves plus the new standards made the pools at Atlantis totally inadequate. A new, much larger pool needed to be built as there would probably be more calves born every two to three years.

However, the marine park was already losing money. The small population in Perth and its isolation from other centres meant that attendance at shows could not remain very high. The cost of electricity was much higher than expected and more staff were required at the park than originally allowed for. The park was running at a loss of three to four hundred thousand dollars per year. The extra two million dollars needed for the new facilities made it certain that the park would close.

On 12 August 1990 the Atlantis dolphins gave their last performance at the marine park.

Now the problem was what to do with the dolphins at Atlantis. There were a few choices available:

1. Moving the dolphins overseas.

2. Moving the dolphins to the east coast of Australia.
3. Putting them down (euthanasia).
4. Releasing them into the wild.

The first choice would be expensive and stressful to the dolphins and would probably involve splitting the group. It was also unlikely that the wildlife authorities would give permission for the animals to be shipped out of Australia.

The second choice was not possible as there were no resorts on the east coast that had facilities for that number of dolphins. The marine park at Adelaide had recently closed down, flooding the Australian market with bottlenose dolphins. Any place that would have had room for extra dolphins had already taken some from the Adelaide marine park.

The third choice was never seriously considered. The dolphins had been taken out of the wild by humans in the first place. Now that conditions had changed and it was inconvenient to keep them, it seemed very unreasonable to have them put down.

The fourth choice was examined in detail. Never before had a large group of dolphins which had been in captivity for so long been released. Some of the dolphins had been bred in captivity and had never experienced living in the ocean. If the dolphins were just turned out into the sea they would surely perish.

Nick Gales was sure that with enough time and resources the dolphins could be successfully released back into the wild. Splitting the group to release some and keep a smaller group to perform was also an option but it was not considered right to split the group, as a large family unit would have a better chance of successfully integrating back in the wild.

Nick visited many places in many different countries

A mother and calf. It was not considered a viable option to split up the dolphins and finally the decision was made to release them into the wild.

researching the chances of successfully releasing the dolphins. He discovered that he would need time and two million dollars to prepare and release the dolphins under controlled conditions. CALM had given a period of grace of only twelve months for the new standards to be implemented.

Tokyu Corporation, the company which owned and financed Atlantis Marine Park, was approached. They agreed to the costs of the planned release with the understanding that this would be the end of their financial commitment. If further financial support was required or the release did not go as planned, other sponsors would have to be sought.

The Long Haul 5

The preparations for the release had many aspects. The territorial behaviour of the wild dolphins in the area had to be assessed. The dolphins had to be taught to hunt for themselves both individually and as a pack. They also had to become accustomed to the high level of bacteria and internal parasites, such as worms, to which they would be exposed in the wild. Because they would need to be followed up in the wild once released, they needed obvious identifying marks and radio transmitters had to be fitted.

First the local wild dolphins were investigated. A photographic bank of dorsal fins was established. The dorsal fin of each dolphin is different, as each has slight differences in shape and nicks. In twenty-three trips, seventy-three dolphins were identified. At least

The different shapes and nicks of dolphins' fins made it relatively easy to keep track of the movements of the wild dolphins.

half of these dolphins were seen two or more times. This showed they were territorial. The wild dolphins were observed to have a *fission-fusion* social organisation. This means individuals would come together in groups for a while and then split up again.

Interestingly, wild dolphins sometimes come into rivers where there is fresh water. In Western Australia dolphins have been spotted as far up the Swan River as Garrett Bridge, which is about thirty kilometres inland and is freshwater. Dolphins can survive for a few days in fresh water or a week or two in water with reduced salinity. In the sea dolphins extract metabolic water (the fresh water in the living tissues) from the cells of their prey to get their freshwater needs.

All the dolphins had been dewormed on arrival, and their health monitored carefully whilst they were in captivity. They had been fed a variety of frozen fish, including sardines, whiting, squid and yellowtail, and were also given a vitamin supplement. In the wild they would be catching live fish and their parasitic load would increase tremendously. They would also be exposed to a few external parasites as the water would not be chlorinated. This, however, would not be a major problem as dolphins' bodies are so streamlined there are few attachment sites for parasites.

When the dolphins were due for a feed, fresh live fish were thrown into the pool. At first the dolphins were confused but they soon worked out that this was a new food source and it was quite fun to have a chase.

The addition of chlorine to the pool was halted. This did not appear to affect the health of the dolphins. Unfortunately the handlers could not see the dolphins in the water, which had turned green and

Kia and Nakita hardly visible in the green pool.

murky, so chlorine was reintroduced while the dolphins were kept in the pool. The level of chlorine and water purity was always very important for the dolphins. The total level of chlorine could not go above 0.5 parts per million, which is about half the concentration aimed at in a human family swimming pool. Free chlorine is not a problem but when it combines with certain impurities in the water it can be extremely toxic. Most of the chlorine in the pool was free chlorine because of fresh water flushing through the system.

Water was pumped to Atlantis from a bore about eighteen metres below ground in the nearby Two Rocks Marina. This was good quality salt water which was free of impurities, having been through nature's own sand filter. This water was pumped to a settling tank before being pumped to the dolphin pools. Here it was circulated through high-pressure sand filters ten times in every twenty-four hour period. Additional salt water was pumped in and completely replaced the old water in the pools every twenty-four to forty-eight hours.

While living at Atlantis each dolphin had been subjected to blood tests every eight weeks. Blood was taken from the tail vein on the underside of the fluke. Blood tests were performed more regularly as the time for release grew near so the health of the dolphins could be closely monitored. Before, with daily training, the interaction between dolphins and handlers had been much greater. Now it was time to wean the dolphins of their liking for human companionship.

It was decided that the dorsal fin of each dolphin would be marked with a number. This would enable fishermen and boaters to identify any of the dolphins they sighted after the release. A virtually painless method of freeze-branding was used. A metal number was cooled in liquid nitrogen then held against the dorsal fin for a few seconds. When it was removed the number was 'burnt' into the skin of the dorsal fin.

The mothers were caught and branded first so they would realise their grown calves would not be hurt. Mila was still a very protective mother even though Nakita was quite large and if she thought anyone was interfering with her baby, she would rush to her defence. She was held while Nakita was caught and marked.

The dolphins were moved to a huge sea pen at Two Rocks Marina. This was a delicate procedure, with the dolphins being transported in slings, two at a time, in a gently-driven vehicle. Frodo and Nero were moved first, followed by the others, with Mila and Rani, who were pregnant, being last and treated very gently. Water was poured over the dolphins along the way to ensure their skin did not get dry.

The main sea pen was 100 metres long by 40 metres wide with an access to the ocean. To start with, the access was blocked by two large stainless steel gates.

Three of the trainers signalling to the dolphins from a movable pontoon at Two Rocks Marina.

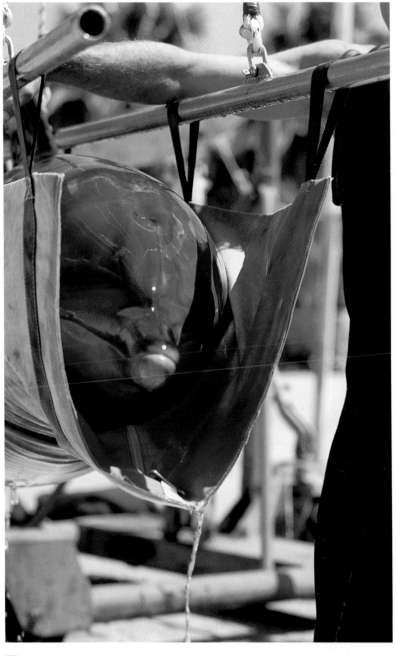

Mila in a sling ready for the delicate task of being transported.

Five smaller training pens, each measuring 4 metres by 4 metres, were installed. Movable pontoons would allow Nick and his team to move the dolphins into a smaller area for health checks or any other procedures. In the sea pens the dolphins were able to experience the ocean with all its sounds and tidal waters.

Dolphins can move through the water at speeds of sixteen to thirty-five kilometres per hour, so fish have little chance of escape. The streamlined body of the dolphin is designed for a gentle, uninterrupted flow of water over it. When this laminar flow is interrupted, the dolphin can adjust its shape to decrease its resistance through the water.

Nick feeding Kia, Echo and Nakita. Kia's chin is battered from feeling her way around the Two Rocks Marina.

The dolphins had to learn to hunt collectively as dolphins do in the wild, herding schools of fish between them so they could all have a good feed. This was quite different from catching fish one at a time. A school of yellowtail fish was supplied but at first the dolphins were very wary of what appeared to be strange new creatures swimming around with them. After all, they thought fish came singly, and not in groups, so these funny moving things should be avoided. In fact the dolphins were never observed feeding on the school.

The dolphins were trained to follow a boat within the training pools. In addition they were shown how to

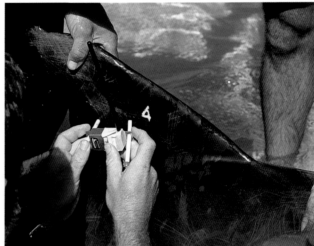

Above left: A plate on Frodo's fin.

Above right: Nick fitting a radio transmitter to Rani. Note the tooth rakes on her skin from the other dolphins.

slide onto a special deck to be examined quickly. They were trained to come to the boat when a sound was made with a special auto recall device. The dolphins should be able to hear this sound over quite a distance. It was hoped that once the dolphins had been released they would return to the boat on command so their progress and health could be checked.

To monitor their progress without interfering with their behaviour it was decided that radio transmitters would be fitted to the adults. No radio transmitters were fitted to the juvenile dolphins because it was assumed that they would stay with their mothers. Each dolphin had an injection of local anaesthetic in its dorsal fin and two holes drilled through the cartilaginous plate so radio transmitters could be fitted. These would be out of the water whenever the dolphin broke the surface, allowing a signal to be picked up. Altogether these special waterproof radio transmitters cost twelve thousand dollars but the expense was readily justified. It would be imperative to follow up on the dolphins to learn if a return to the wild would be a viable option for future dolphins.

Darkest before Dawn

6

There is a saying: 'It is always darkest before the dawn.' This reflects how often in life we encounter most of the problems just before the completion of a project. In the attempt to release the dolphins this certainly proved to be the case.

On top of having to close the marine park, the team now had dolphin problems. Just after the closure of the park Karleen became ill. She had acute gastritis (a very painful inflammation of the stomach) and despite all the best medical attention, she died. Kia was only two-years-old at this stage, but luckily she was an independent individual and coped despite the loss of her mother.

Rajah, who was sixteen-years-old, was the next to become sick. At first it was thought that he had a

Rajah leaping out of the water at Two Rocks while being chased by the other males.

virus. Perhaps when the chlorine had not been added to the water he had succumbed to the higher level of infectious organisms present. He was given a course of antibiotics but he did not respond. Nero and Frodo had recently matured sexually and they clubbed together to eliminate Rajah from the group. If he tried to approach the other dolphins he was chased away. It appeared as though something physical was ailing him but it was hard to tell how much his social isolation may have been contributing to his ill health.

Numerous tests, including blood tests, were done on Rajah but nothing was discovered. Perhaps he had stomach ulcers. An attempt was made to do a gastroscopy: optic fibres were inserted through the dolphin's mouth to try and view his stomach. A dolphin's stomach has several compartments and it was impossible to see anything. He was treated symptomatically as though he had ulcers. Rajah finally did respond but this may have been due to a social change in the group rather than any physical effect.

Lulu had always been the dominant dolphin of the group. She could be distinguished from all the others as she was the only dolphin that showed no scratch marks from the other animals' teeth. She gave birth to another calf in late 1989. After the tragedy of her first calf being stillborn everyone was delighted. Unfortunately this second calf died after only one week.

Shortly after this event the group ousted Lulu. She was chased away from the group and had rake marks from their teeth where they had bitten her whenever she tried to come close. One morning a few weeks later she was found dead at the bottom of the pool. Though she had been quite badly battered by the other dolphins, her injuries were not sufficient to have killed

Mila in the sea pen with the radio transmitter fitted.

her. It was thought that the stress of being relegated from the dominant group member to a total outcast was just too much for her to bear.

One thing that did happen after her death was that Rajah began to show an improvement in health. We question whether the dolphins may have coped better with these problems if they had been in the wild. With the almost limitless space of the open ocean in which to avoid each other, they may have been under fewer social pressures.

The preparations for the release continued. Rani and Mila were pregnant once more. It was hoped that the dolphins could be released before the calves were born. It was not possible to prevent further pregnancies as the dolphins needed to be kept together while being prepared for their release. Male dolphins are very strong and can break through all but the most robust barriers to get to females. Sterilisation was not considered a viable option as it was potentially dangerous. All in all, the fertility of the captive dolphins was becoming a problem.

Sterilisation of the dolphins would be very hazardous. Using anaesthetics on dolphins is immensely complicated as their breathing operates in a reverse way to ours. They expire forcefully and inspire passively, using their full lung capacity. The testes on the male are not external and sterilisation would be a complex procedure involving anaesthetics. The other alternative, hormonal control of fertility, is frequently accompanied by side effects in large mammals.

There were some lighter moments during the long preparations. Mila gave birth to a calf earlier than expected, on 28 November 1991. The staff discovered the extra dolphin in the pool one morning and were overjoyed to find it was a male. The new arrival was named Luca.

Nick decided to keep fit by swimming in the sea pen. Nakita and Kia had other ideas. They thought it fun to put their rostrums on his feet and push him around in the water. Nick's need for exercise was forgotten. The pleasure of interacting in this way was made all the more precious because it had been initiated by the dolphins.

The two dogs that had been guard dogs at Atlantis would also play with the dolphins. Mr Chips, the Doberman, and Sami, the German Shepherd, loved to swim in the sea pen. The dolphins would circle the dogs trying to get them to swim out to deeper water. Mr Chips would attempt to leap on their backs but they were much too fast and agile for him.

Mr Chips, the Doberman, playing with Rani at the Two Rocks Marina.

Kia playing with baby Luca. He appears large because she is still quite small.

7 *Away They Go— Or Do They?*

The team felt they had done as much as they could to prepare the dolphins for their release. The date for opening the gates of the sea pen to the open sea was set for Monday, 13 January 1992. The team knew the dolphins very well by this stage. They expected them to be very cautious and reluctant to leave the known confines of their sea pen.

The gates were opened at 8.00 a.m. and everyone sat back to watch events unfold. After a few hours with no reaction from the dolphins, the handlers decided to lend a hand. They fed the dolphins fish from an inflatable boat as they headed out through the gates. The dolphins followed them to the gates, but then turned back. The motor boat was brought out next. It was thought that the dolphins, recognising the engine noise, would be happy to bow ride with the motor

The gates of the sea pen are open and Echo is reluctant to swim out.

boat. They had been trained to do this within the confines of the sea pen in recent months. Again nothing happened. The gates themselves were removed in case their presence was making the dolphins wary.

The dolphins' cooperation was limited. They had put up with people trying to lure them out the gateway but they finally had enough. They returned to the shallow area of the sea pen away from the gateway to the open sea. The gates were left off and as darkness came the handlers left, not knowing what they would find by morning.

The next day was a repeat of the first.

On Wednesday Rajah followed the boat out through the gateway. He was no longer part of the happy family group and because of this was possibly keen to explore the big, wide world outside the pen. He left the boat and soon swam off beyond the range of the radio receiver. In the following days he was seen interacting with two wild dolphins on one occasion and a group of five on another.

It took another three days before the rest of the dolphins were prepared to venture out of the sea pen. They followed the boat out but made sure they kept it in sight for the entire duration of the trip. This was

The boat at Two Rocks Marina with several dolphins bow riding.

Rajah at sea.

what the team had been hoping for. They were slowly introducing the dolphins to the open sea under controlled conditions. At last things were going according to plan!

Next morning when the team arrived at the sea pen all the dolphins had left. Unfortunately Echo had taken a wrong turn and separated from the rest. She was sighted just south of the sea pen in Two Rocks Marina. The team set off to capture the reluctant Echo. She made a bid for freedom but their detailed knowledge of that area of the coastline gave the humans the edge. Echo was put in a sling and hoisted onto the boat.

In the meantime the other dolphins had been located with the help of the radio transmitters. Echo was taken by boat to join the rest of the group which was about three kilometres north of the marina. Two days later the dolphins had split up into a few groups—Nero and Frodo in one group; the females, Rani, Mila, Kia, Echo and Nakita in another; and Rajah still out on his own.

The dolphins would not respond to the auto recall once out at sea. The project boat went out daily trying to pick up signals via the radio transmitters. Because the dolphins had split up, the research team was kept very busy trying to monitor their progress. Fishermen and boaters were encouraged by the media to report any sightings of dolphins to Nick Gales and the team. Sightings were reported from Shark Bay in the north to Busselton in the south. This showed the dolphins were ranging over an area of over one thousand kilometres.

The receivers picked up signals from Mila and Frodo. Kia and Nakita were seen playing with a few wild dolphins. Then many days went by with no sightings. Help was requested from the police, who supplied a helicopter. Nick Gales tied a radio receiver to the outside of the aircraft and they flew low from Garden Island, just south of Perth, to Lancelin, 100 kilometres north. A further survey was conducted in a fixed wing aeroplane from Albany, 500 kilometres south, to Jurien, 200 kilometres north.

Signals were picked up from all the dolphins carrying transmitters except Rajah. Nero and Frodo were at Carnac Island, just north of Garden Island, and Mila and Rani were together a bit further north. The position of the dolphins was given to the boat, which set out for a more detailed reconnaissance. The dolphins avoided the project boat. This was regarded as a positive sign, showing the dolphins were adapting to their new-found freedom.

However, Rajah followed the boat back into the sea pen after one of its outings. He was found to have lost weight and so he was kept in the pen and fed up to better condition.

Then a call from Fremantle alerted the team to another problem. Echo was in the shallows, having separated from the group again. There were reports that she had been bothering fishermen and begging for fish. It was found that she too had lost weight and she was brought back to the pen for feeding up. Another call, this time from Margaret River, 250 kilometres

Frodo out at sea.

Mila at Ocean Reef.

south of Perth, reported Frodo was fine, playing in the surf and approaching humans, but not to beg for food.

Mila was observed around Ocean Reef, thirty kilometres south of Two Rocks, with her calf Luca, who was seen to be very thin. The next day he had disappeared. The team tried to keep track of Mila but her transmitter failed and they had to rely on reports from fishermen. Fifteen-year-old Mila had been sighted on her own and it was presumed that Luca was dead. The team eventually caught Mila and found that she too had lost condition. She was brought back to the sea pen.

Now three dolphins, Rajah, Echo and Mila, were back in the sea pen at Two Rocks. From here they were moved to a pen at Hillary's Boat Harbour where they will form part of the attractions at Underwater World. They no longer perform a major show for the public but are still drawing the public's interest. Perhaps in the future these dolphins will be allowed a bit more freedom. It is hoped they will learn to work around the boats so they may be taken out to sea and brought back again. It is likely they will continue to be fed and cared for as long as they cannot cope with a return to the wild. This would appear to be the best option for these particular dolphins.

The remaining five dolphins are still out in the wild—three of the original seven captured and two that were born in captivity. To the best of our knowledge, they are coping well. The two youngsters, Nakita and Kia, were reputedly sighted with a group of wild dolphins.

Some of the developments have been unexpected. Although it was thought that the group would stick together, they have instead split into many groups. It was thought that Mila was likely to be successful in the wild as she had a great aptitude for catching live fish. Rajah, who was the first to leave and seemingly had the most to gain from freedom, did not cope. The dolphins which had been born in captivity appeared no less able to adapt than the others.

All these things are teaching us more about dolphins. We do not understand them as well as we would like but with each new experience we learn more about them. Hopefully learning more about such a popular species will make us realise how much there is in nature we do not understand. It is important for us to preserve as many things as possible in their natural environment as we have no idea what may prove irreplaceable in the future.

Although not all the efforts at release were a success, it is good to know that at least some of the dolphins are back in their rightful place in the wild.

Glossary

Auto recall device   A device making a noise which carries over a long distance. The dolphins were conditioned to come to the boat when they heard this noise.

Autopsy   Study and dissection of a dead animal to determine the cause of its death.

Blowhole   The hole at the top of a whale or dolphin's head through which it breathes.

Bow riding   Swimming in the wave at the front of a boat caused by the speed of the boat moving through the water.

Break-away hoop net   A net attached to a hoop by a very thin weak thread so it can break away from the hoop very easily.

Bridging signal   The use of a sound or signal to demonstrate that a reward has been earned.

Calf   Term used to describe a dolphin from birth to adolescence.

CALM   The governmental organisation for conservation and land management in Western Australia.

Cartilaginous plate   A fairly tough skeletal structure found in the dorsal fin of a dolphin.

Dominant   Strongest animal or the one which commands the most respect.

Dorsal fin   The fin on the back of a dolphin, whale or fish.

Euthanasia   Killing something in a painless way such as by an injected overdose of anaesthetic.

Fertility   Capacity to produce young.

Fission- fusion social organisation   Individuals come together in groups of different sizes then split up and join other groups on a continuous cycle.

Fluke   The horizontal tail fin of a whale or dolphin.

Foetal calf   The developing but as yet unborn calf.

Free chlorine   The chemical chlorine when not combined with any other chemical.

Freeze-branding A painless process of marking the skin of an animal by applying a very cold metal symbol to the surface.

Gastritis Acute inflammation of the stomach.

Gastroscopy An internal examination of the stomach using optical fibres.

Infectious organisms Viruses, bacteria and fungi which can be passed from one animal to another and cause disease.

Laminar Flow The flow of water parallel to the body of the animal. If the animal is streamlined, the flow of water is smooth.

Marine biologist Someone who studies marine organisms.

Melon The 'forehead' region of the dolphin.

Metabolic water The water found in living cells of any organism.

Navigate To find the way.

Organism Any living thing.

Parasites A variety of living creatures, such as fleas and worms, which obtain their nutrition from the animal they live on or in.

Pontoons Floating platforms. Nets suspended from these allowed the trainers to move the dolphins to a confined area for any procedures they undertook.

Random interrupted reinforcement The process of giving a break during a training procedure and allowing the animal to do something it enjoys before returning to training.

Rapport A positive communication between two parties.

Rostrum The extended mouth area of the dolphin.

Reconnaissance A look to see what is happening.

Settling tank A tank where water is stored allowing particles to settle to the bottom.

Snap frozen Frozen very rapidly.

Sterilisation Prevention of the production of offspring by an operation which physically removes reproductive organs or blocks the passage of their products.

Stillborn The animal is already dead when born.

Territorial Staying within certain boundaries.

Time out Being ignored or left out of any activity.

Toxic Poisonous.

Treat symptomatically To treat an animal for the symptoms it is displaying without knowing the cause of its illness.

Ultrasound The examination of internal structures using high frequency sound waves and collecting an image on a screen.